**Abou

Roger Stevens visits schools, libraries and festivals performing his work and running workshops for young people and teachers. He is a National Poetry Day Ambassador. He has published forty books of poetry for children and his latest collections are:

The Waggiest Tails
with Brian Moses

'Fun to read but also perceptive, sometimes moving'
BOOKS FOR KEEPS

Apes to Zebras (An A-Z of Shape Poems)
with Sue Hardy-Dawson and Liz Brownlee

'Captivating series of animal shape poems… there's something to inform and delight children of all ages'
THE GUARDIAN BEST NEW CHILDREN'S BOOKS

Joe Decie is a highly regarded cartoonist.
His latest novel, published byJonathan Cape,
is **Collecting Sticks** (Observer Graphic Novel of the Month)

THE
POETRYZONE

A Celebration of 20 years
of children's poetry

Selected by
Roger Stevens
Illustrated by
Joe Decie

troika

For my children, Paul, Kate and Joseph.
And their children, Lily, Ruby and Sam. For Merlin.
For my wife, Jill, for all her help with all my writing
and music projects. For my parents and for Jill's parents.
For our dogs, Jasper and Judy (herself a wonderful poet).
For Roy and Martin at Troika for their enthusiasm for this
project and for all the children and teenagers who have sent
poems in to The Poetry Zone over the last twenty years and
the teachers and parents who have encouraged them.
Thank you.

Published by TROIKA

First published 2018

Troika Books Ltd
Well House, Green Lane, Ardleigh CO7 7PD
www.troikabooks.com

Copyright © individual poets 2018
Illustrations copyright © Joe Decie 2018

The moral rights of the authors and illustrator have been asserted

A CIP catalogue record for this book is available from the British Library

ISBN 978-1-909991-83-5

1 2 3 4 5 6 7 8 9 10

Printed in Poland

Contents

Acknowledgements

The editor and publishers would like to thank all those who have contributed to this Anthology and kindly given permission to reproduce copyright material.

Poems listed below have previously been published as follows:

John Agard: Rooms, *The Rainmaker Danced* (Hodder 2017)

Clare Bevan: Bourbons, *Let's Recycle Grandad* (A & C Black 2008)

Gerard Benson: Shouting at the Ocean, *Shouting at the Ocean* (Hands Up Books 2009)

Debra Bertulis: How Not to Impersonate Your Mum on the Telephone, *I Bet I Can Make You Laugh* (Bloomsbury)

James Carter: The Big Things, *Time-Travelling Underpants* (Macmillan Children's Books)

Jane Clarke: Drop in the Ocean, *Don't Get Your Knickers in a Twist* (Macmillan Children's Books 2002)

Paul Cookson: Turn That Racket Down!, *Turn That Racket Down* (Red Fox 2001)

Graham Denton: Pupil Troubles, *Read Me at School* (Macmillan 2009)

Matt Goodfellow: A Different Kind of Poem, *The Same Inside* (Macmillan 2009)

Chrissie Gittins: Wasp on the Tube, *The Humpback's Wail* (Rabbit Hole Publications)

David Harmer: The Lone Teacher, *Elephant Dreams* (Macmillan)

Steven Herrick: When We Grow Up, *Pookie Aleera is not my boyfriend* (University of Queensland Press 2012)

Trevor Millum: The Dark Avenger, *Double Talk* (Kingston Press)

Michaela Morgan: A Llama Alarmer, *Shouting at the Ocean* (Hands Up Books)

Brian Moses: Days, *Lost Magic* (Macmillan)

Grace Nichols: Who Makes her Own Bed? *Cosmic Disco* (Frances Lincoln 2013)

Trevor Parsons: What Poets Eat for Lunch, *Let's Recycle Grandad* (A & C Black 2008)

Brian Patten: Geography Lesson, *Juggling with Gerbils* (Puffin 2000)

Rachel Rooney: Unfair, *The Language of Cats* (Frances Lincoln)

Coral Rumble: The First Bit, *Breaking the Rules* (Lion Children's Books 2004)

Nick Toczek: Ecology Rant, *Me and My Poems* (Caboodle Books 2008)

Phillip Waddell: Mixed Emotions, *Love, Hate and My Best Mate* (Hodder Children's Books 2004)

Celia Warren: Pelican, *The Works 5* (Macmillan Children's Books 2006)

Colin West: My Auntie, *It's Not Funny When You Look At It* (Hutchinson 1984)

Steven Withrow: Reading Braille, *It's Not my Fault!* (Bloomsbury)

Bernard Young: I Am the Kid, *Look Out! The teachers are coming* (Macmillan 2005)

Every effort has been made to trace copyright holders but in a few cases this has proved impossible. The editor and publishers apologize for these cases of unwilling copyright transgression and would like to hear from any copyright holders not acknowledged.

Introduction

Young poets produce wonderful work – in their schools and at home – but it is seen by a very small audience, if at all. I launched **The Poetry Zone** twenty years ago because I wanted to create somewhere for children and teenagers to send their poems and, just as importantly, see them published; somewhere they could share their poetry and where it would be taken seriously.

Since 1998, **The Poetry Zone** website has received more than a million visitors and I've read and published around 30,000 poems by children and teenagers from all around the world. It has featured interviews with a large number of children's poets and included advice and information for teachers, reviews of new poetry books and has run about a hundred competitions, for which publishers have kindly donated prizes.

I have never allowed advertising on the site. **The Poetry Zone** has never made any money. It has always been a labour of love. My reward has been seeing children enjoy everything that poetry has to offer – whether they are writing it or reading poems written by others and commenting on them.

So, welcome to the book that celebrates **The Poetry Zone's** twentieth anniversary. The collection features poems generously donated by some well-known and acclaimed fellow children's poets and, course, by some of the brilliant young poets who have contributed to **The Poetry Zone**. All royalties will be going to a children's charity.

The book aims to be a loose anthology put together in not-too-strict an order, but it begins with poems for (and by) younger children. And at the end you'll find some more challenging pieces for (and by) older children and teenagers.

As I've put the book together, one thing has stood out more than any other. The poems by children are every bit as good as the poems written by grown-ups! We have a wealth of talented young writers all over the world – a cause for optimism and hope for the future of poetry. It has been great fun collecting the poems together and I hope you enjoy them.

Roger Stevens

Night Time

Rosie King (aged 10)

I lay in bed thinking
"What could I do tomorrow?"
I could go swimming and do a lap in ten seconds
I could fly to Venus and see an alien
I could go to the South Pole to see a penguin
I could go to the woods and meet a rabbit
Or...
I could just write poems on the Poetry Zone!
What should I do?

Shhh...

Roger Stevens

I know where Mum
Hides her chocolate biscuits

I'm not going to tell you
Because it's a secret

There were five in the packet
But now there are four

I wonder if she'll notice
If I have just one more?

The Octopus

Eric Ode

How odd to think the octopus
has not a bone inside her.
The smallest space in any place
is just enough to hide her.
A corner in a sunken ship,
a coffee can,
a shell.
She tucks her boneless body in
and every arm as well.
A very tricky thing to do
if you have one
or maybe two.
But what an awkward sort of state,
the octopus has eight!

In the Zoo

Freddie Alderson-Jenkins (aged 6)

The Lions roar
The Snakes hissssss
The Monkeys go peek-a-boo
The Zebra goes clippity-clop
The Hyena growls
The Meerkat squeaks
The Eagle squawks
The Elephant trumpets
The Giraffes chew the leaves
The Blue Whale sings his whale song
The Polar Bear moans loudly
The Penguins chitter chatter
The Wolves howl
The Zoo Keeper smiles with pride.

A Llama Alarmer

Michaela Morgan

A llama, a llama
will keep your sheep calmer
yes that's what a llama will do.
It's not just a charmer
it can be an alarmer
and see off a hungry bear too.
There's no need of armour
if you keep a llama.
It's more than a big snooty sheep.
So go get your pyjamas
you weary old farmers
at last you can stop counting sheep.
Yes a llama, a llama's
a friend to the farmer,
a friend to the chicken and sheep.
No panic and drama
if you have a llama -
just sweet dreams, quiet fields...
   and deep sleep.

The King of the Jungle

Sam Rozenberg (aged 13)

He stands on top of the hill
With his head held high.
He makes sure no one will defeat him,
Or his jungle.
He comes out with a big loud roar,
While the wind is blowing his mane.
He runs fifty miles per hour,
To catch his yummy prey.
His fierce attitude tells him he can do anything.
That's is why he isn't a chicken.

Later when he is tired,
He comes home to his family,
His cubs and wife.
He makes sure they aren't hurt,
And sends them off to bed.
He kisses his wife goodnight,
Then sends her to bed.
The Moon is out and he gives one roar,
"Stay away from my family! Goodnight."

Lost

Sue Hardy-Dawson

I cannot find my Cedric
I put him in a pail
Left him in the garden
And now there's just a trail

I searched inside the sandpit
And underneath the hedge
Put up little posters
And asked all of his friends

I really can't stop sobbing
After meeting many bugs
No-one is quite as loving
As Cedric my pet slug

Little Ants

Nana Safo (aged 6)

Little ants munching on plants
as quietly as they could
so that nobody would see them
If anybody was about to
the party of ants
would creep and hide

Wasp on the Tube

Chrissie Gittins

If I knew how I got here
I wouldn't have *commmmmmmmmme*,
those doors banged shut,
that was the end of my *funnnnnnnnnnn*,
I'm buzzing around
and causing a *hummmmmmmmmmmm*,
they're all looking up
and they think I am *dummmmmmmmb*.
I want to escape,
get back to the *sunnnnnnnnnnnnnnnnnn*,
that boy's going mad
and grabbing his *Mummmmmmmmmm*,
if we weren't in a tunnel
I know they'd all *runnnnnnnnnnnnnnnnn*,
at last, King's Cross,
my tube journey's *donnnnnnnnnnnnnnne*.

The Grand Old Count of York

John Foster

The Grand Old Count of York
He had ten thousand bats.
He kept them in his wardrobe
Hanging from his cloaks and hats.
And when he went out they flew out.
And when he went in they flew in.
And when they were neither in nor out
They haunted his neighbours' flats

Batty About Bats

Philip Ardagh

I'm batty about
bats
I'm head-over-heels in love with
somersaults.
Encores leave me crying out for
more.
I think that flying insects' joints are the bee's
knees
and that Oxygen is a
gas...
But ice cubes leave me
c-c-cold

Skipping

Roger Stevens

It's an easy mistake
To make
But it's best not to skip
with a snake

It may seem a bit
Of a lark
But it's best not to swim
With a shark

If you don't want to look
Like a fool
Best not to play ball
With a bull

Jaguar

Indigo Moss (aged 7)

With its mighty roar, tons of stripes and spots galore,
Summoning all the beasts, with its beauty
   and clashing teeth.
Sister of lions and brother of the tiger,
Everyone stares at this stalking hider.
Up high, in the trees, stealing honey from the bees,
Nursing their cubs till fair and plump,
And after six months, teaching them how to hunt.
And when they are two, here is what they will do,
They will leave their mother all alone, until she makes
   another clone.
I, myself, love the jaguar, I treat it like golden armour.
You see I have a pet, a male.
Guess his name?
Yes, that's right, it's…
JAGUAR!

The Divers and the Dolphins

John Rice

Ah, just look at them,
aren't they beautiful.
So graceful, so sleek
as they swim around the boat –
poking their snouts up
to break the surface,
then diving straight down,
blowing bubbles all the time.
And look at all their different colours.
I'll bet they could fetch things.
I've even seen one
dive deep down to a wrecked ship.
Look at its oval eye, so large, so glassy.
And listen; I'm sure they're communicating.
Not 'talking' as we know it,
but they're certainly intelligent.
Strange how those land-leggers feel they have
to dive underwater from time to time.

Pelican

Celia Warren

Pelican, Pelican,
Why so big a beak?
Is that where the words live
That you would like to speak?
Long words, special words,
Words to keep for best,
Words you've loved forever
Since your egg-days in the nest?

Pelican, Pelican,
I have words like that,
Safe inside my word-cage
Underneath my hat:
Dodecahedron,
Sycamore, rose,
Paprika, chameleon,
Words such as those.

Pelican, Pelican,
Open up your beak,
Share your thesaurus,
I long to hear you speak.
Ungainly and cumbersome,
You're not a pretty bird,
But, Pelican, your name is
My favourite feathered word.

Guillemot

John Hegley

I am a guillemot
I use my bill a lot.
I get the fish out of the wet, I eat my fill a lot.
I live on ledges, vertical edges, eating-wise
I do not know what veg is.
Don't give me sherbet,
give me a turbot;
my appetite for fish, I cannot curb't.
I am a guillemot
I know the drill a lot.
I drill in to the drink and get the drink and not the ink
upon my quill a lot.
I do my speccy reccy
from my rocky window sill a lot.
I am a guillemot.
I am a diver, ocean arriver
underneath I go, I am no skiver.
Did you know that I can go so deep, I have been
    seen from the porthole of a submerged submarine,
    one hundred and thirty metres under?

I didn't think so - miss it and blink so!
I come in hard and I'm able to sink, so.
I don't do nesting, when I am resting
I can sleep while I am standing on one leg
and, so it doesn't roll off
when I stretch my wings or stroll off
I've got an egg
that is conical and eccentrically weighted
so that it doesn't fall off the cliff face into the water
with all the jellyfish and all the other fish.
I am a guillemot,
I find the fishes tend to lose one-nil a lot.
But, I'm not a greedy bird.
I am sustainable
self-restrainable.
I am a guillemot.
Am I not.

The Dark Avenger

A poem for two voices

Trevor Millum

My dog is called The Dark Avenger
Hello, I'm Cuddles
She understands every word I say.
Woof?
Last night I took her for a walk.
Woof! Walkies! Let's go!
Cleverly, she kept three paces ahead.
I dragged him along behind me
She paused at every danger, spying out the land.
I stopped at every lamp-post.
When the coast was clear she sped on.
I slipped my lead and ran away.
Scenting danger, Avenger investigated.
I found some fresh chip papers in the bushes.
I followed, every sense alert
He blundered through the trees, shouting, "Oy, Come 'ere!
Where are you?
Something – maybe a sixth sense – told me to stop.
He tripped over me in the dark.

There was a pale menacing figure ahead of us
Then I saw the white Scottie from next door
Avenger sprang into battle, eager to defend his master.
Never could stand terriers!
They fought like tigers.
We scrapped like dogs.
Until the enemy was defeated.
Till Scottie's owner pulled him off. Spoilsport!
Avenger gave a victory salute.
I rolled in the puddles.
And came to check I was all right.
I shook mud all over him.
"Stop it, you stupid dog!"
He congratulated me.
Sometimes, even The Dark Avenger can go too far.
Woof!

Looking After Ted

Roger Stevens

I'd love to play at Minecraft
Make a den in next door's shed
I'd love to make a wooden raft
And watch the dog play dead
I'd love to throw the giant ball
And stand upon my head
Or run along the garden wall
But I'm looking after Ted

I'd love to make a secret den
Underneath Mum's bed
With a box to hide my chocolate in
But I'm looking after Ted
Ted's my favourite Grandpa
And I am only three
I'm looking after Ted
And Ted's looking after me

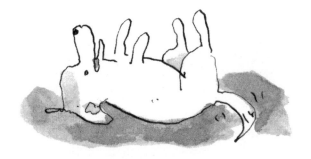

January Poem

Catherine Benson

Flake on flake
the snow
rewrites the garden.
Word on word
the poem
settles on the page.

The Visitor

Valerie Bloom

Cold fingers clawed the face of earth,
Bold winter strutted round,
Bare branches trembled in the wind,
Their leaves mulching the ground.
Dancing snowflakes chuckled in the
prancing north-east breeze,
Algid rivers stood still, crippled,
Aged women coughed and wheezed.
Sheep shivered in the snow-bound wasteland,
Steep and icy were the paths,
In the houses, people huddled,
Skin slowly cooking round the hearths.
Then it happened, one clear morning
When the bite of cold was sore,
That there came a gentle knocking
On the weatherman's cottage door.
He got up and shambled out to
See, his heart began to sing.
By the door, a young girl smiling,
"Hi," she said, "my name is Spring."

The First Bit

Coral Rumble

I love the first bit of the morning,
The bit of the day that no one has used yet,
The part that is so clean
You must wipe your feet before you walk out into it.
The bit that smells like rose petals and cut grass
And dampens your clothes with dew.

If you go out you will bump into secrets,
Discover miracles usually covered by bus fumes.
You will hear pure echoes, whispers and scuttling.

I love the first bit of the morning
When the sun has only one eye open
And the day is like a clean shirt,
Uncreased and ready to put on;
The part that gets your attention
By being so quiet.

Days

Brian Moses

Days fly by on holidays,
they escape like birds
released from cages.
What a shame you can't buy
tokens of time, save them up
and lengthen the good days,
or maybe you could tear out time
from days that drag, then pay it back
on holidays, wild days,
days you wish would last forever.
You could wear those days with pride,
fasten them like poppies to your coat,
or keep them in a tin, like sweets,
a confection of days
to be held on the tongue
and tasted, now and then

Hard Work

Jill Townsend

In the garden
I weed and sow,
water the plants
so they will grow.
I put the tools
back in the shed
and go to sleep
on a flower bed.

Mr Rain

Mike Johnson

Lightning.
Thunder.
On River Street,
under damp lamps,
droplets dance.
Splosh, splash
Another flash
and, there,
ungurgling himself
from flowing toes,
to spill over his
meniscus brim,
drips Mr Rain.
Lifts his bowler hat,
tips
a liquid-whiskered cat.
Mr Rain – with soggy moggie –
songs along the cobbles;
refrains, then claims their drain.
He takes his waterfall bow.
She makes one wet, "Miaouw."
Will we see them again,
I wonder?
Lightning.
Thunder.

Who Makes Her Own Bed?

Grace Nichols

Who makes her own bed
and lies on it?
Who plays her own music
and belly dances to it?
Who designs her own dress but gets
flying-fishes to stitch it?
Who washes and combs her own hair
in her own blue waves?
Who keeps both her jewels and her bones
in her watery cupboards?
Who else but sea – coming to the edge of shore
to lift us off the shells of our toes.

Mint

Roger Stevens

Cinnamon
Smells of snuggly bedtimes
Hot chocolate drinks
And granny's candles

Chilli peppers
Will burn your tongue
Be careful

Mint smells of summer
Like sunshine after rain
Mint cheers food up
And makes
A refreshing cup of tea

I love mint the best

Drop in the Ocean

Jane Clarke

Sloshing around
in life's restless sea,
there's a drop in the ocean –
and that drop is me.
Riding the waves,
or washed up on the shore,
I'm a miniscule drop
amongst zillions more.
I'm a drop in the ocean
of life's restless sea –
but there'd be no ocean
without drops like me

Shouting at the Ocean

Gerard Benson

Last week the sea was whispering,
hushing and shushing the beach,
sifting its salty secrets into the sand.
But this evening the moon is full
and the sea's found its voice; it bellows and roars,
sings aloud, booms in the Smugglers' Cave.
And me? I'm shouting right back at it,
shouting at the ocean. Full-voiced.
I fill my lungs and let go.
I call out my name over and over,
then other words. Roller! Smash! Crash!
Wow! Boulder! Ocean! Ocean! Ocean!
The wind comes whistling and lifts my words
and carries them over the waves.
Wow! Roller! Ocean! Ocean! Ocean!

Cookin' Up a Universe

Shauna Darling Robertson

Particle soup!
Particle soup!
Start with a big pot
of particle soup.

Add in some photons, a few cosmic strings
and out pops a jungle and six chicken wings.

Mix in some quarks and a mini black hole,
which may create rain clouds or loud rock 'n' roll.

Chuck in some bosons: one X and a Higgs.
Result? Iron ore and a kilo of figs.

Three light neutrinos, a gluon or two
will often as not yield a tree kangaroo.

Stir in a lepton, a handful of WIMPs,
then watch as the room fills with glassware and shrimps.

Gravitons, gluons and monopoles (four)
will either make peas or a long civil war.

Choose your ingredients, roll out the dice
and pray that the world you've just made will taste nice.

Particle soup!
Particle soup!
Let's make a big pot
of particle soup.

It's Magic

Chiamaka Uchegbu (aged 7)

A little bedtime when I see a sparkle
It glimmers and shimmers and won't stop
Then I wonder what it is
Maybe it's a...

A fairy
With two sparkling wings that shine all the time,
A little dress all covered with ribbons and bows
As well as hair that flows and flows

Or a shooting star
Shining as bright as the sun
With points as sharp as knives
Mostly golden on the outside

Or a firefly
Glowing with delight
Flying at a slow pace at the dead of night
Not being cautious of where it's going

Of course it's not
When something glows
It can only mean one thing
IT'S MAGIC!

The Flippertigibbet

A. F. Harrold

Send for the flippertigibbet.
Bring the flippertigibbet here.
Roll it out, bring it forth.
Uncover the flippertigibbet.
Let everyone see it.

Look at the flippertigibbet.
See how the sun shines on it.
It's a good-looking flippertigibbet.
The finest-looking flippertigibbet.
Look! Look closely!

Now put the cover back on.
Re-cloak the flippertigibbet.
Push it, heave it, haul it away.
Put it back where it came from.
That's enough for today.

Geography Lesson

Brian Patten

Our teacher told us one day he would leave
And sail across a warm blue sea
To places he had only known from maps,
And all his life had longed to be.

The house he lived in was narrow and grey
But in his mind's eye he could see
Sweet-scented jasmine clinging to the walls,
And green leaves burning on an orange tree.

He spoke of the lands he longed to visit,
Where it was never drab or cold.
I couldn't understand why he never left,
And shook off the school's stranglehold.

Then halfway through his final term
He took ill and never returned,
And he never got to that place on the map
Where the green leaves of the orange trees burned.

The maps were redrawn on the classroom wall;
His name was forgotten, it faded away.
But a lesson he never knew he taught
Is with me to this day.

I travel to where the green leaves burn,
To where the ocean's glass-clear and blue,
To all those places my teacher taught me to love
But which he never knew.

The Chosen One

Roger Stevens

I love being chosen
To get the PE kit out

The mats have to be carried (not dragged)
(Miss Moss is very particular about this)
From the store
And the crates with the bean bags, and balls,
and coloured ribbons
Arranged along the front of the stage
And the benches laid in order

And I love being chosen
To put everything away
At the end of the lesson
Everything neatly stacked
In its place
(And sometimes we miss
The first ten minutes of Science)

But I'm not so keen
On the bit in between

Pupil Troubles

Graham Denton

There once was a teacher, Miss Wright,
Whose lessons affected her sight.
Through all of her classes
She sported dark glasses—
Her students were simply *too bright*!

The Lone Teacher

David Harmer

We've got a new teacher
he wears a mask
and a big wide hat.
He comes to school
on a silver horse
and rides around the field
all day.
Sometimes he says,
"Have you seen Toronto?"
We tell him
we haven't been to Canada
but is it near
The Panama Canal?
We did that in Geography
last term.

At four o'clock
he rides off into the sunset
and comes back the next morning
in a cloud of dust.
We wonder if
he will ever come and teach us maths
like he said he would
when he first arrived.
Perhaps then he'll tell us his name
not keep it a secret
because my dad always asks me,
"Who is that man?"

(This looks like a children's poem doesn't it?
But it's really for grandmas and grandads.
Especially if they lived in the UK in the 1960s.)

New School Rules

by Roger Stevens (aged 10¾)

The loser of the hundred metres
is the winner
The last one picked
is the captain of the team
Eating doughnuts in class
is compulsory
If you win a million pounds and then wake up
it's not a dream

In maths
there's no long division
There are no dates
in history
and the school prize is always given
to the world's biggest Notts Forest fan
(that's me!)

I Am the Kid

Bernard Young

I am the kid who says "Break's over"
at exactly 10.44.
I am the kid whose job it is
to knock on the staffroom door.
We haven't drunk our coffees yet!
I wish you'd go away!
That child is such a pest!
are the sort of things they say.
They're never pleased to see me.
How the insults fly!
But I don't care if they're put out.
I love to hear them sigh.
I am the kid who says "Time's up."
The kid they don't adore.
Because I am the kid whose job it is
to knock on the staffroom door.
(And I am the kid
who's looking forward
to upsetting them again
at precisely 1.04)

STAFF
ROOM

NO CHILDREN

Knock
Knock
Knock

How Not To Impersonate Your Mum On The Telephone

Debra Bertulis

Swimming
The worst day of the week
Mum refused to write a note
So…

I practised in the mirror
The facial expression
That high-pitched screeching whine
"My Benjamin is so ill today!"
"My Benjamin has such a fever!"

I looked like mum
I sounded like Mum
I was Mum!

So…
Picked up the telephone…
Dialled the number…
Deep breath and…
"Hello!
This is my Mum speaking!"

Oops!

Unfair

Rachel Rooney

She picked the fight
but now she cries.
I know I'm right.
She's telling lies
but now she cries
for sympathy.
She's telling lies
and Dad blames me.
For sympathy
she dabs her face
and Dad blames me.
I'm in disgrace.
She dabs her face,
she gets a hug.
I'm in disgrace,
she's looking smug.
She gets a hug,
I want to cry.
She's looking smug
I'm sure that's why
I want to cry.
I know I'm right.
I'm sure that's why
she picked the fight.

When We Grow Up

Steven Herrick

I thought it was a simple question, really.
Ms Arthur asked each of us to stand up, in turn,
and say what we want to be
when we grow up.
The first five students said
   Teacher
then Alastair said
   Pilot
and we went slowly around the class
   Builder
   Doctor
   Truck driver
   Writer
   Vet
   Architect
   Soldier
and when it was my turn
I stood up
and in a very clear voice, said,
   A Dad.

Everyone giggled
as if I'd said something rude,
or silly.
The bell rang for recess
and I sat down again,
red-faced and confused.
It was the truth.
I wanted to be a Dad.
I've never seen my dad
and I wouldn't wish that
on anyone.

Fear

Indigo Moss (aged 8)

Fear is a shadow dancing on the wall
It is like an everlasting horror movie planting nightmares
    in your mind
It is dismay, like a black stone gnawing at your heart
It makes you want to cling to your teddy and pull the
    covers over your head.

Fear is the monster hiding under your bed
It is like the knot in your stomach
It is uneasiness of knowing something bad will happen
    and you can't face it alone
It makes you want to scream for your dad.

Fear is the creak of the staircase
It is like the howling of the wind
It is panic, like the trees tapping on your windows
It makes you want to disappear.

TAP
TAP
TAP

Bourbons

Clare Bevan

My little brother thought
That the scary ladies
With evil eyes
And snakes in their hair
Were called
Bourbons.

So

Whenever our Aunties
Asked us round for tea,
We would cover our faces
And shout:
"DON'T LOOK AT THE BISCUITS –
THEY'LL TURN YOU TO STONE!"

And our angry Aunties
Would glare at us
Like GORGONS.

My Auntie

Colin West

My auntie who lives in
Llanfairpwllgwyngyllgogerych-
wyrndrobwllllantysiliogogogoch
Has asked me to stay.

But unfortunately
Llanfairpwllgwyngyllgogerych-
wyrndrobwllllantysiliogogogoch
Is a long, long way away

Will I ever go to
Llanfairpwllgwyngyllgogerych-
wyrndrobwllllantysiliogogogoch?
It's difficult to say.

Grandad on My Scooter

Justin Coe

Grandad's still a bad lad
A Trojan and a trooper
And no man can move faster than
Grandad on my scooter
Woe betide you if he's behind you
And you don't hear his hooter
Pension power, ninety miles an hour
It's Grandad on my scooter
He never brakes, just overtakes
And always gets there sooner
A rare dare devil, freewheeling rebel
Grandad on my scooter
Straight from the past, so super-fast
He's flying to the future
Where it's all downhill, chased by The Bill
Grandad on my scooter

A Bit of a Power Thing

Jan Dean

I am the Space-Time Continuum Mum,
The cold blue universe rests in my hands.
I am the Space-Time Continuum Mum,
I shrivel planets to burning sands.
When I speak stars shiver and quiver and quake,
When I roar suns blaze hotter then crumble and break.
All of the galaxies worship, revere me,
Nothing that lives doesn't bow down and fear me.
So crawl through the dust, do not dare to come near me!
For I am the mother of all mother stuff
The cosmos falls still when I shout, "Enough!"
So, little one, little one, listen and hear me:
I am the Space-Time Continuum Mum
And you will obey my decree,
So finish your homework this minute
And clean up your room before tea!

Turn That Racket Down!

Paul Cookson

Turn that racket down! Are you going deaf?
Turn that racket down! I'm trying to concentrate!
Turn that racket down! Do you call that music?
Turn that racket down! It's making my head ache!

Turn that racket down! I can't hear myself think!
Turn that racket down! It all sounds the same!
Turn that racket down! They can hear it down the street!
Turn that racket down! It's driving me insane!

I need to get this done!
Can't you see I'm trying to work?
It sends me round the bend!
It's driving me berserk!

Switch that music off right now!
You know it drives me mad!
I need to get my homework done
So… TURN IT DOWN, DAD!

The Poet Called Gorringe

Roger Stevens

There was a young poet called Gorringe
Who was after a rhyme for orange
With a tinge of regret
Said, I've not found one yet
As he sucked on a peppermint lozenge

Nearly a Haiku

Roger Stevens

This poem was nearly a haiku
But the syllable count came out wrong
I was going to write about losing in love
In fact this was nearly a song
Then a tanka, a cinquain – though they're both overrated
I considered a sonnet
But that's too complicated

Then I had to watch the match on TV
And there were baddies to beat on my Play Station 3
And my best friend came round and we talked until late
And Mum said, Bedtime! That poem must wait.

This poem was nearly a haiku
But it turned out much too long
So, in the end, I opted for this
And I'm sorry that in the end the whole thing

turned out to be rather disappointing

A Different Kind of Poem

Matt Goodfellow

a different kind of poem
might be short, long
or somewhere in-between
a different kind of poem
might chime with rhyme
or it might not
a different kind of poem
might have an unconventional and seemingly ungainly rhythm
making it flow quite differently from those you are used to
a different kind of poem

             might   pattern   the
      page   how   it
wants to
entirely   disregarding   what
                                             any
      other   poem   is doing

A different kind of poem
might discuss issues
which you find awkward or
uncomfortable
a different kind of poem
might do some, none
or all of the above
but
a different kind of poem
is still
a poem
isn't it?

What Poets Eat for Lunch

Trevor Parsons

Around one o'clock, when they're ready for lunch,
poets decide on which sandwich to munch.
Some always go for fillings that rhyme
forgetting that taste should come first every time.
So lamb may be chosen with soft bits of clam
or ham thickly smothered with cranberry jam.
A bap or a wrap with slivers of gammon
with frogs' legs, ducks' eggs and the roe of a salmon.
Salami, pastrami and a nice bit of brisket,
fat from a rat and a sprinkling of biscuit.
Lychees and cheese with a garnish of fleas –
all the above are quite likely to please.
Other poets, time after time,
choose alliterative fillings, rather than rhyme.
So tiny tomatoes, tuna and tongue,
lugworms and lentils with lemon and lung,
Brussels, baloney, bananas and beet –
any of these would be right up their street.
Mind you, some are less fickle,
liking pickle and free verse.

Snack Attack

Liz Brownlee

We're
aliens, we're
coming, through
interstellar space, racing
meteors and comets at a hyper-warp-speed pace.
Our latest information leads to Earth – our destination.
Just as soon as we arrive, the freshest food – we'll eat it live.
Crunchy, chewy and nutritious –
we're told Earthlings are

DELICIOUS!

Love in All Shapes

Samuel (aged 10)

Love is unique for everyone
You'll find it in many shapes and sizes.
Love may be small or tall,
Fat or thin,
Abstract or not,
Creative and serious,
Funny and emotional,
Fearless or fearful.
For you, love may be simple,
But for me it's everything.

Romeo and Juliet

Elsie King (aged 12)

Romeo and Juliet
Loved each other very much
The hatred between their families
wasn't enough to keep them apart
Their love was deep,
as deep as a pool,
a pool of darkness,
a never ending pool,
a pool with crystals,
crystals that shone,
a pool of wonder,
wonder why,
why their families fought
Why did they have to be born,
born into those families
that hated each other?
Why oh why
did they have to be born,
born into these families
that hated, hated, hated
hated each other?

Valentine from a Scientist

Celina Macdonald

It's not in one's heart but in one's head
That stops one from acting inane.
It's in the head that one feels fear
Or love, or hate or pain
The heart has nought to do with emotions,
It merely pumps blood through your veins.
So it might not sound that romantic but:
I love you with all my brain.

Dreams

Joshua Seigal

The blue sky dreams of fluffy clouds
The prisoner dreams of an open door
The footballer dreams of cheering crowds
The soldier dreams of an end to war
The snake dreams of flying like a flock of birds
The bird dreams of burrowing like a mole
The book dreams of being more than words
The broken man dreams of becoming whole
The insomniac dreams of having dreams
The dreamer dreams of being awake
The battlefield dreams of an end to the screams
The birthday girl dreams of her birthday cake
The follower dreams of leading the pack
One dreams of becoming two
Going up the hill, Jill dreams of Jack
And me? I dream of you.

Anna

Roger Stevens

She's a fragile ghost
She's a white angel
She's scruffy trainers and tight jeans
She's diet coke and burnt toast
She's a waterlogged moon and a firefly glow
She's an explosion of stars
She's the heart of the forbidden forest
She's the secret behind the waterfall's rainbow
On a long road with no turning she's the first bend
She's a map of secret pathways in a foreign land
She's a white starfish on a sunburnt beach
She's my best friend

Spying On My Neighbour

Violet Macdonald

I've been spying on my neighbour for ages,
If he drives in or out I see,
It took me a year and a half to find out,
My neighbour was spying on me.

Metropoem

Celina Macdonald

I am wri ting this po em
Tick tick tick tick tick tick tick
To a met ro nome
Tick tick tick tick tick
So if I get just one beat wrong
Tick tick tick tick tick tick tick tick
It' ll hit me with a ve ry long
Stick tick tick tick tick tick tick tick tick.

Violet and Celina Macdonald began sending poems to The Poetry Zone when they were children. And carried on well into their teens. Their poems we're so good, I even used a few in some of my anthologies. They were around 12 or 13 when they wrote these.

The Other Ark

Roger Stevens

Spare a thought for the ark
made by Noah's mate, Frank
When the flood waters rose
Frank's ark sank.

Shed a tear for the grabus,
and the bongobodon
Such beautiful beasts
such a shame they are gone

The minzies, the throppies
the hallomalinber
Such a pity that Frank
Used sub-standard timber

The glorious goyku,
the mellifluous jigger
How we all wish that Noah
had made his ark bigger

The Sculpture

Pragun Pudukoli (aged 12)

I feel something is staring at me.
It's behind me. Don't know what

it is, just have to look behind.
I turn and look at the thing

that was staring at me. It is
a sculpture made of trash that is

as tall as a rabbit. Was it a kid
who created this in a few minutes?

Or some artist who wanted to create a
piece of abstract art? And why, oh why

would this park be the perfect place
for this sculpture? I think that it's lost.

Might have fallen down when the artist
was strolling through this park. I hope he finds

it – the piece of abstract art that I think I will
never, ever properly understand.

The Artist

Fatema Zahra Mithwani (aged 9)

Emerald green trees
all thick with
promises
tower up like
monuments,
as the golden sand
ripples with
pride,
showing its willingness
to receive
a sprinkling of
life-gifting
seeds

The soft crooning of
the pearlescent
waves
beckons you
tenderly
to this majestic
land,
that is
filled to
the brim with
ingenuity

The serenity of
these kingly
waters,

knitted
mindfully with
turquoise aquamarine,
has tranquility
holding out its
hand like
a bold
companion

A tropical
wonderworld
where dolphins
dance and whales
wander, sea turtles
shift, and stingrays
surround
a breathtaking
bounty
of cradling
coral

Hearts sown
harmoniously with
threads of glorification –
flora, fauna, and
human alike,
living to the
rhythm
of the
Almighty's
awe-inspiring
artistry

Reading Braille

Steven Withrow

I sail my fingerships
Over a paper sea
I do not see

I sail my fingerships
Across a dotted alphabet
Shaped like wave caps

Forward and back
I do not stop
Until I touch bottom

Of the great, wide page.

Stupid Humans

Andrea Shavick

Smoke in the air
Rubbish on the ground
Chemicals in the river
Sewage in the sea

Graffiti on the walls
Solvents up nostrils
Bottles in the gutter
Guns in the shops

Drugs on street corners
Hormones in the water
Toxins in the atmosphere
Additives in the food

What have we done?
And how long do you think
It will take stupid humans
To become extinct?

Ecology Rant

Nick Toczek

Ecology rant. Ecology rave.
This isn't a joke. It's really grave.
Go energy save, go energy save.
This planet's our home. It isn't our slave.
We'll change our style, be bold, be brave
And energy save, and energy save.
I'll use less water when I shave
Or when I brush my teeth and bathe.
I'll energy save, I'll energy save.
I'll share my car with Sue and Dave.
And close that door! This isn't a cave!
Let's energy save, let's energy save.
There's power in fire and wind and wave
To give us the things we really crave
And, in return, we'll energy save.
We'll cut our waste from birth to grave.
It's how the whole world should behave
And energy save, and energy save.
Ecology rant. Ecology rave.
Let's energy, energy, energy save.

Stopwatch

Harshita Das (aged 12)

I hate deadlines
I hate timers
I hate things that restrict my time
That make it so I have to make haste
But when I stop to think about it
I realize
My life is running on a stopwatch

The Big Things

James Carter

Early evening
I'm sitting in my favourite tree
gazing at the moon
in the pale summer sky
just thinking
Thinking about the big things:
like time
and infinity
and the cosmos
and how our little misty marble
of a planet
keeps spinning around
in that great murky soup
we call space

When Keith –
my next door neighbour –
peers over the fence
and says "What you doin'
up there then?"
And I say
"Well, Keith – I was thinking
about the unstoppableness of time
and the smallness of me
and the wopping great bigness of space
and things."
And Keith says "Oh, right."
And I jump down
from the tree
climb over the fence
and say "Keith?
Do you ever think about time
and space and life
and what it all means and stuff?"
And Keith says "Fancy a game of footie?"
And I say "Do you, Keith?
And do you think about
how the planets all turn together
like the cogs of a massive cosmic clock?"
And Keith says "Look, you playing footie or what?"
And I say "No seriously, Keith,
do you think about it?"
And Keith says, "I'll go in goal."
And I say, "Oh...whatever."

The Owl

Iona Mandal (aged 11)

I saw you through the glassware
Our family heirloom.
Smudged round the rims
A camera out of focus
Caked with dust
Like a leftover painting.

I always failed to climb your eyes
So steep, yet deep
Endless cavity
Churning oceans
Eerie, steel green
Phosphorescent glow
Crypt in every chamber.

What your black beak had killed that day
Now stood in heaven
Watching us glance.
You with your soul
I with my heart
You with no end
I with no start.

Wishes had space to become dreams
In your clear, feathered heart
Words had books to fill
Your wisely soul.

Oxygenated silence
Peered through your eyes
A mirror of your emotions.
Monoxidic noise
Pierced through your heart
Serrated knife edge
Cleaving open hatred.

Only destiny held
What your talons would drop
Only moonlight would seep
Through your wings.

I saw you through the corner of my eye
Before you swooned and swooped
Then flew
Away.

Perfect

Harshita Das (aged 12)

There is darkness
In each one of us
A tendency to kill
A desire for pain
A hunger for suffering
A greed for more
A blindness to honesty
A thirst to choose wrongly
Nobody is flawless
But to shroud that darkness
With light
Is what makes a person
Perfect

Mixed Emotions
Philip Waddell

My first shows in helping and not in hurting.

My first is in heartless – not caring or kind.

My next – in supporting and not subverting.

My second – in anger and malice you'll find.

My third shows in giving and not in cheating.

My third starts the trouble I spread everywhere.

My fourth is in friendship and twice in greeting.

My fourth lives in misery, torment and fear.

Solutions: **Love**, Hate

My Dreams
A Poem about Slavery
Lucy Cohen (aged 10)

My dreams are here to stay,
Not to be crushed,
Despite other people's actions,
Because of my colour.

Their hearts of cold iron,
Making me do this,
Rocks balancing on my head,
My dreams are here to stay.

Stench of defeat
In my bones,
Everyone is frozen with fear,
My dreams are here to stay.

I'm missing the colour of the sun,
Thinking of the blue sky,
When will my freedom appear?
My dreams are here to stay.

Hope is a fragile seed.
Right now,
My dreams are here to stay,

Lost in a sea of nameless faces,
I need to be remembered,
Here I am.
My dreams are here to stay.

Am I Good Enough Now?

Ellie (13)

Concealer, foundation, blusher,
Am I good enough now?

Bs, and A*s
Am I good enough now?

Rings, Designer Clothes, the most expensive phones,
Am I good enough now?

Mansions, riches, diamonds,
Am I good enough now?

I changed for you.
AM I GOOD ENOUGH NOW?

A Less Lonely Night

Aditi Jain (aged 13)

Make my one night less lonelier
I know it's starting but
I think you need to know
Even though you will find it
Not important. These words
Insist that I say so
I know this will take time
Each and every phase
Are running to get spilled out
Because I have to rewind, pause and replay
And queue them up, so that
I do not hesitate. While talking to you
I need to tell you about days
When my pillow soaked up my tears
Every night

I need you to know about how
Each weekend I have re-lived
My childhood with my grandmother
Telling tiny naughty tales of herself
I need to say about the day
I've attempted to write the perfect
Suicide note and was terrified
To find it in my mom's trembling hands
I have to tell you about those
Google search histories
That said "how to differentiate
Between depression and sadness"
Make my one night less lonelier
Listen to me I will
Surely feel better

Seven Sided Hexagon

Praniti Gulyani (aged 14)

six hexagons, carved we—
on the crystal ball of our world
for each month we spent together
I stepped down from my roller coaster,
and told you—
that I'd left my footprints on the sky
you looked.

six hexagons, carved we—
on the crystal ball of our world
for each month we spent together
I told you, one night—
that the sky had lost a constellation
you looked.

six hexagons, carved we—
on the crystal ball of our world
for each month we spent together—
I claimed, one afternoon
that I could weigh the evening
you smiled and
got me the weighing machine
you looked.

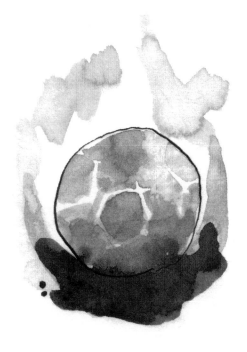

six hexagons, carved we—
on the crystal ball of our world
for each month we spent together—
pausing before the road not taken
I asked you to check
for sticks and stones
yet, you colored a bit of breeze
with the bitter hues of sour grapes
merely mentioning the ointment
just in case my feet bled

six hexagons, carved we—
on the crystal ball of our world
for each month we spent together
your intrigue, when I ask Santa
for a seven sided hexagon.

Truth

Harshita Das (aged 12)

Sometimes the truth can be hard
Hard to consume
Hard to digest
Hard to move on from
But it is the truth
Conceal it
And you only delay the pain
Conceal it
And you only feel guilty
Conceal it
And you have to tell a thousand more lies
And yet despite this
Sometimes it is necessary
Crucial
To make sure the person does not run away
From the bitter truth
Sometimes it's better to lock it away

Rooms

John Agard

In the keeping room
we keep many things.
Exactly what, I'm not telling you.
In the sleeping room
naturally we sleep
and hope for a dream, perhaps two.
In the peeping room
we take a peep at life
while life peeps back out of the blue.
In the leaping room
we like to leap about.
It's known as doing the kangaroo.
In the heaping room
we heap our junk and stuff
for recycling into newer than new.
In the weeping room
we weep our hearts out
till the past has received its due.
That's when we return
to the keeping room
and keep our thoughts to ourselves.

Just One

Laura Mucha

One more mountain, just the one,
one more trip away with Mum,
one more apple rhubarb pie,
one more amber-lilac sky.
One more chocolate – plain and dark,
a peacock and a national park,
Arctic iceberg, Shetland sheep
and one more really good night's sleep.
One more day of blazing heat,
one more friend I'd like to meet,
one more bike ride, one more hike, I'd
talk to every bird and bee,
I'd soak them up, I'd set them free
with paint, with words, perhaps a song.
Life is short and life is long,
so quickly please, before it's gone,
just one more poem.